Name

Introduction

This book is designed for children who have not previously attempted written comprehension. Some children will not yet feel secure in reading independently and many will benefit from extra support. Use the opening pointer (◖) to introduce the text and then read the text with the children. Discuss the content, eliciting or explaining the meaning of any new words.

After reading the text, read each question with the children and elicit oral responses. Questions are presented in two parts to suit the concentration level of most children in Years 2 and 3. Model how to answer the questions in written form, rephrasing the children's answers if necessary, before they begin writing. Many questions require simple retrieval of information. Some involve inferential understanding, where the child must recognise cause and effect – for example, inferring how a character's feelings motivate their actions. Others test the child's ability to understand new words by recognising similarity to familiar words or from contextual clues. It may be helpful to provide a simple dictionary and show the children how to look up words.

As the children become familiar with formal comprehension, they may start to attempt questions independently. However, your availability – to help with reading and interpreting questions, for example – will build children's confidence. If you are marking the children's answers without access to the separate **Teacher's Guide**, allow some leeway. Where a child's answer may not represent the most obvious response, it may still be a logical, justifiable and valid interpretation of the text.

First published in 2015

Tenth impression 2020

Copyright © Schofield & Sims Ltd 2015

Author: Celia Warren

Celia Warren has asserted her moral right under the Copyright, Designs and Patents Act, 1988, to be identified as the compiler and author of this work. Any text not otherwise attributed has been written either by series author Celia Warren or by the publisher Schofield & Sims and is copyright © Schofield & Sims 2015. This includes translations and retellings as well as completely new texts that have been written for the series.

Big red boots (page 4) is from *Come into this Poem* by Tony Mitton, published by Frances Lincoln Ltd, copyright © 2011. Reproduced by permission of Frances Lincoln Ltd. **British garden birds** (page 6) is from the 'Wildlife explorers' section of the Royal Society for the Protection of Birds website (www.rspb.org.uk) and is reproduced by permission of the RSPB. **The Enormous Crocodile** (page 8) is from *The Enormous Crocodile*, published by Jonathan Cape Ltd and Penguin Books Ltd, and is copyright © Roald Dahl 1978. It is reproduced by permission of the author's agent, David Higham Associates Ltd. **The wizard's dog** (page 10) is copyright © Bernard Young and is reproduced by permission of the author. **Plop meets a boy scout** (page 14) is from *The Owl Who Was Afraid of the Dark* by Jill Tomlinson. Text copyright © The Estate of Jill Tomlinson 1968. Published by Egmont UK Ltd London and used with permission. **I love my darling tractor** (page 16) is from *I Had a Little Cat – Collected Poems for Children* by Charles Causley, published by Macmillan Publishers Ltd. It is copyright © Charles Causley 1994 and is reproduced by permission of David Higham Associates Ltd. **Keeping warm in bed** (page 18) is from *Snug as a Bug* by Mal Peet and Elspeth Graham, and is copyright © Mal Peet and Elspeth Graham 1994. It is reproduced by permission of the authors. **An adventure for Brave Mouse** (page 20) is from *Brave Mouse* by Jeremy Strong, published by Pearson. It is copyright © Jeremy Strong 1996 and is reproduced by permission of the author's agent, David Higham Associates Ltd. **The four friends** (page 22) is from

When We Were Very Young by A. A. Milne. Text copyright © The Trustees of the Pooh Properties 1924. Published by Egmont UK Ltd London and used with permission. **What makes me move?** (page 24) is based on *Understanding Science: Our Bodies*, copyright © Schofield & Sims Ltd 2007. **A very small beetle** (page 26) is from *Omnibombulator* by Dick King-Smith. It is reproduced by permission of A P Watt at United Agents on behalf of Fox Busters Ltd. **Birdsong lullaby** (page 28) is from *Singing Down the Breadfruit and Other Poems*, published by Red Fox Poetry Books in 1994. It is copyright © Pauline Stewart and is reproduced by permission of the author. **Beyond the castle walls** (page 30) is reproduced from *Time Travellers: Knights and Castles* by permission of Usborne Publishing, 83–85 Saffron Hill, London EC1N 8RT, UK. www.usborne.com. Copyright © 1995 Usborne Publishing Ltd. **Stop thief!** (page 32) is from *Stig of the Dump*, written by Clive King and published by Penguin. It is reproduced by permission of the author's agent, David Higham Associates Ltd. **Jeremy Strong's World** (page 36) is an abridged version of 'Jeremy Strong's world: poetry, accidents and bedtime scribbles' by Jessica Salter, 31 May 2013. It is copyright © Telegraph Media Group Ltd 2013 and is reproduced by permission of the Telegraph Media Group Ltd.

British Library Catalogue in Publication Data:

A catalogue record for this book is available from the British Library

Commissioning by **Carolyn Richardson Publishing Services** (www.publiserve.co.uk)

Design by **Oxford Designers & Illustrators**

Printed in the UK by **Page Bros (Norwich) Ltd**

ISBN 978 07217 1220 8

Contents

Icons used in this book

This 'pointer' icon marks the brief introduction that sets the piece of writing in context and provides useful background information.

📖 This icon indicates that it would be useful for you to have access to a dictionary.

Big red boots

Tony Mitton's poem uses strong rhythms and rhymes, and is perfect for reading out loud. Listen out for the foot-stamping chorus. Does it remind you of anything?

Big red boots, big red boots.
One of them squeaks and the other one toots.
One of them hops and the other one stamps.
Big red boots take long, wet tramps.

Boots, boots, big red boots.
One of them squeaks and the other one toots.

Big red boots on busy little feet
start out shiny, clean and neat.
Big red boots, oh, yes, yes, yes,
end up muddy in a terrible mess.

Boots, boots, big red boots.
One of them squeaks and the other one toots.

Boots, boots, big red boots,
squelch through mud and trample roots.
Big red boots say, "Look! Oh gosh!
What a great puddle there . . . Yay! SPLOSH!"

Tony Mitton

Schofield & Sims **First Comprehension** Book 1

Part 1

1 Colour the boots to match the title of the poem.

1 mark

2 a) Read the first line aloud and make your fingers 'walk' like feet to the rhythm of the words.

b) Which of the words below describe how the boots move? (ring **two**)

scuffing   stamping   hopping   tiptoeing

2 marks

3 Where do you think the boots are walking? (ring **one**)

along a city street   in a supermarket   down a country lane

1 mark

4 Write **two** words that describe the person wearing the boots. For example, is the person young or old, happy or sad, lively or lazy?

_____

2 marks

5 Name **two** noises that the boots make again and again.

_____

2 marks

Part 2

6 Why does the person wearing the boots say 'oh, yes, yes, yes', when the boots get muddy?

_____

1 mark

7 What do you think the person is doing in the very last line of the poem?

_____

1 mark

8 Which word sounds like the noise of walking through mud? (ring **one**)

scratch   squelch   thud   sink   shake

1 mark

9 Why do you think the poet writes 'SPLOSH!' in capital letters?

_____

1 mark

page 5
total out of 12

British garden birds

 In this text, five common garden birds introduce themselves. They tell you about how they look, where they live, and the things they eat. You may see these birds near your home or school.

Blackbird

- Male blackbirds are black and female blackbirds are brown.
- I eat worms from your lawn.
- My song is one of the best you will ever hear.
- I love to scratch around in autumn leaves.

Blue tit

- I eat caterpillars, nuts and seeds.
- Look for me in trees, but not on the ground.
- I nest in holes in trees, including nest boxes.

House sparrow

- My black bib and face mask mean that I am male.
- I like to live near people.
- My chunky beak is good at cracking seeds open.

Chaffinch

- My red front means that I am a male.
- I live almost everywhere in the UK.
- I eat seeds but feed my chicks on insects.

Robin

- I eat worms.
- I am usually alone in the garden.
- I sing in winter as well as in the spring.

From *Birds*
Wildlife Explorers' website,
Royal Society for the Protection of Birds

Part 1

1 Which bird does **not** like to feed on the ground?

_____

1 mark

2 a) Which **two** birds are likely to be pecking in a lawn?

_____

2 marks

b) What would they be hoping to find?

_____

1 mark

3 A home for a bird's young is called (ring **one**):

a house   a nest   a hole   a burrow.

1 mark

Part 2

4 Which bird feeds insects to its babies?

_____

1 mark

5 The house sparrow has a chunky beak. Ring the phrase that means 'chunky'. (ring **one**)

good for chewing   short and wide   long and thin

1 mark

6 Write one fact that could go under a new heading, 'Duck'. Write the fact as if the duck is talking about itself.

_____

_____

2 marks

7 Explain why a duck would **not** fit in this particular list of birds.

_____

1 mark

page 7
total out of 10

The Enormous Crocodile

 The Enormous Crocodile is a bad, greedy crocodile who likes to eat small children. In this text, he uses a cunning trick to try to catch a child at the fair.

Soon, all sorts of children came flocking into the fair. Several of them ran towards the roundabout. They were very excited.

"I'm going to ride on a dragon!" cried one.

"I'm going on a lovely white horse!" cried another.

"I'm going on a lion!" cried a third one.

And one little girl, whose name was Jill, said, "*I'm* going to ride on that funny old wooden crocodile!"

The Enormous Crocodile kept very still, but he could see the little girl coming towards him. "Yummy-yum-yum," he thought. "I'll gulp her up easily in one gollop."

Suddenly there was a *swish* and a *swoosh* and something came swishing and swooshing out of the sky.

It was the Roly-Poly Bird.

He flew round and round the roundabout, singing, "Look out, Jill! Look out! Look out! Don't ride on that crocodile!"

Jill stopped and looked up.

"That's not a wooden crocodile!" sang the Roly-Poly Bird. "It's a real one! It's the Enormous Crocodile from the river and he wants to eat you up!"

Jill turned and ran. So did all the other children. Even the man who was working the roundabout jumped off it and ran away as fast as he could.

From *The Enormous Crocodile*
Roald Dahl (1916–1990)

Schofield & Sims **First Comprehension** Book 1

Part 1

1 📖 The children 'came flocking' into the fair. What does 'flocking' mean here?

_____

2 marks

2 Who wants to ride on the crocodile?

_____

1 mark

3 What does the child think the crocodile is made of?

_____

1 mark

4 Why doesn't the author tell us the names of **all** the children at the fair?

_____

2 marks

Part 2

5 Why do you think the Enormous Crocodile keeps very still?

_____

1 mark

6 When the Enormous Crocodile is **not** on the roundabout, where does he live?

_____

1 mark

7 What does Jill do when she hears the Roly-Poly Bird's warning?

_____

1 mark

8 Which of these words describe the Roly-Poly Bird? (ring **two**)

quiet   helpful   hungry   loud   confused

2 marks

9 Do you think the Roly-Poly Bird has met the Enormous Crocodile before? Explain your answer.

_____

1 mark

The wizard's dog

 This poem is about a very special kind of dog with a rather unusual owner. Bernard Young, who wrote this poem, often visits schools with his guitar and combines words with music.

The wizard's dog
doesn't bury bones.
He hides stars.

He doesn't go walkies.
He flies.

He doesn't fetch sticks.
He brings back wands.

But he does chase
the witch's cat.

And when his master gets home
he goes crazy
with excitement and love.

So, in many ways,
he is a fairly ordinary
sort of dog.

The wizard's dog.

Bernard Young

Part 1

1 Who is the dog's master?

_____

1 mark

2 What does the dog do with stars?

_____

1 mark

3 Most dogs fetch sticks, but the wizard's dog fetches _____ .

1 mark

Part 2

4 Dogs often chase cats. Whose cat does this dog chase?

_____

1 mark

5 The wizard's dog often behaves just like an ordinary dog. Give **two** examples using your own words.

_____

_____

2 marks

6 Complete this sentence. 'Boy' is to 'girl' as 'wizard' is to _____ .

1 mark

7 Draw a pattern on the wizard's dog's bowl to show what he enjoys.

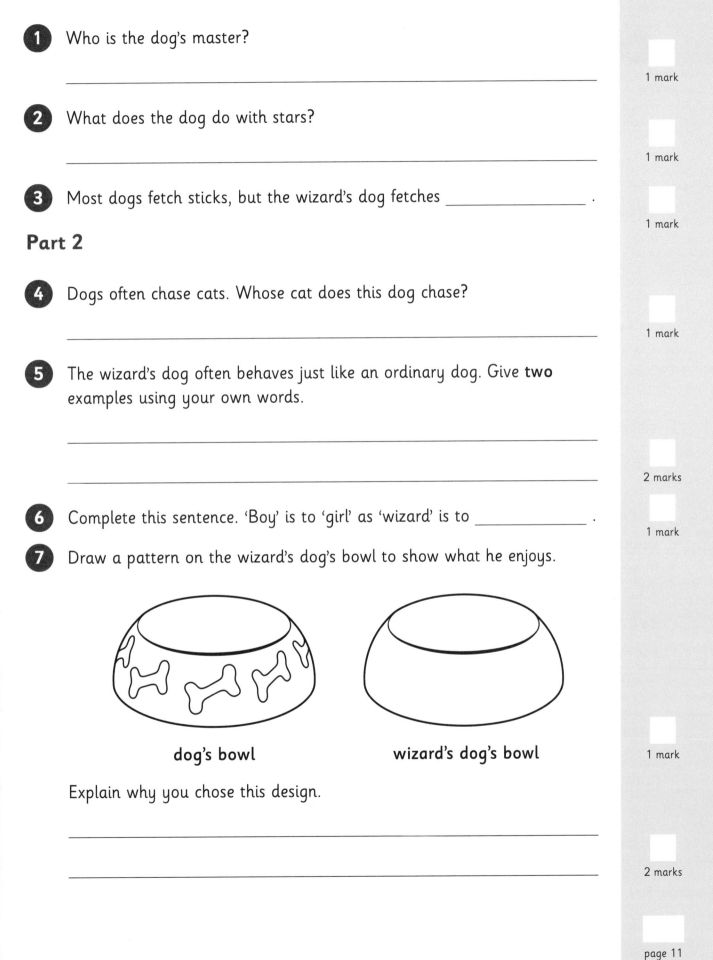

dog's bowl   wizard's dog's bowl

1 mark

Explain why you chose this design.

_____

_____

2 marks

page 11
total out of 10

Dipping into the dictionary

 You can look up words in a dictionary to find the meaning or check the spelling. The words in orange are the 'headwords'. The words in bold purple print are other forms of the headword. Below these is the meaning of the word. If a word has more than one meaning, these are numbered.

secure

firm; safe; free from danger

see

sees, seeing, saw
1 what you do with your eyes
2 to understand

seed *seeds*

a grain from which a plant grows

seek

seeks, seeking, sought
to search for; to look for

seem

seems, seeming, seemed
to appear to be

seize

seizes, seizing, seized
to take hold of roughly; to grab quickly

seldom

not often; rarely

Part 1

1 Choose **two** words to write in the gaps to complete the sentence.

> mean   hear   spell   sing   draw

I look in a dictionary to find out how to _____ words and to find out what words _____ .

2 marks

2 What is the same about the beginning of each word on page 12?

_____

2 marks

3 Choose a word from this dictionary page to write in the gap below. Be sure that it makes sense:

Dan's birthday is in June. It is often sunny and it _____ rains.

1 mark

Part 2

4 When John wrote about looking for his lost toy, he wrote: 'I seeked it everywhere.' John's teacher told him 'seeked' was wrong.

Find the correct word on page 12. _____

1 mark

5 a) Which word would come straight after 'seldom' in the dictionary? (ring **one**)

> soon   supper   select   slim   six

1 mark

b) Why did you choose this word? _____

_____

1 mark

6 The word 'see' is a verb. Other forms of this verb are given in brackets (sees, seeing, saw).

Find **one** other verb in the dictionary extract. _____

1 mark

7 Choose **one** word from the text to replace the words in brackets.

The police officer (quickly grabbed) _____ the man's arm.

1 mark

page 13
total out of 10

Plop meets a boy scout

 Plop, a young barn owl, is afraid of the dark. To overcome his fear, he needs to find out more about it. In this text, Plop meets a boy scout who teaches him that 'dark is fun'.

Plop watched the Boy Scout build up the fire. "Could – could I be a Boy Scout, do you think?" he asked.

"I doubt it," said the Scout. "You're a bit on the small side. I suppose you could be a Cub, but you have to be eight years old."

"I'm eight weeks," said Plop.

"Looks as if you'll have a long wait, then, doesn't it?" said the Scout. "Anyway," – he grinned – "you'd look jolly silly in the uniform!"

Plop looked so disappointed that the Scout added, "Never mind. You can stay for the sing-song tonight."

"Oh, can I!" cried Plop. "That would be soo – super!"

"You'd better go home and ask your mother first, though."

So Plop flew up to the nest-hole – and found his mother waiting.

"Where have you been?" she said. She sounded a bit cross, like all mothers when they have been worried.

"I've been talking to a Boy Scout, and he says DARK IS FUN, and he says I can stay for the campfire, so can I, Mummy, please?"

"Well, yes, all right," she said.

"Oh, super!" said Plop.

So Plop was a Boy Scout for a night. He sat on his new friend's shoulder and was introduced to all the others. They made a great fuss of him and he had a wonderful time. He did not care for cocoa, but he enjoyed a small potato. His friend blew on it for him to cool it, because he knew that owls swallow their food whole, and a hot potato in the tummy would have been very uncomfortable for Plop!

From *The Owl Who Was Afraid of the Dark*
Jill Tomlinson (1931–1976)

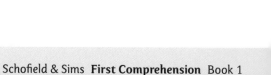

Part 1

1 Choose **two** words to write in the gaps and complete the sentence.

> silly   young   small   naughty   scared

Plop is too _____ and too _____ to be a boy scout.

2 marks

2 Name **two** things that the boy scouts plan to do in the evening.

_____

2 marks

3 Why do you think the boy scouts have a campfire? Think of at least **two** reasons.

_____

_____

2 marks

4 Why does Plop's mother sound cross when Plop returns to the nest?

_____

1 mark

Part 2

5 What does Plop's mother say when she allows him to go to the bonfire? Write her exact words in the speech bubble.

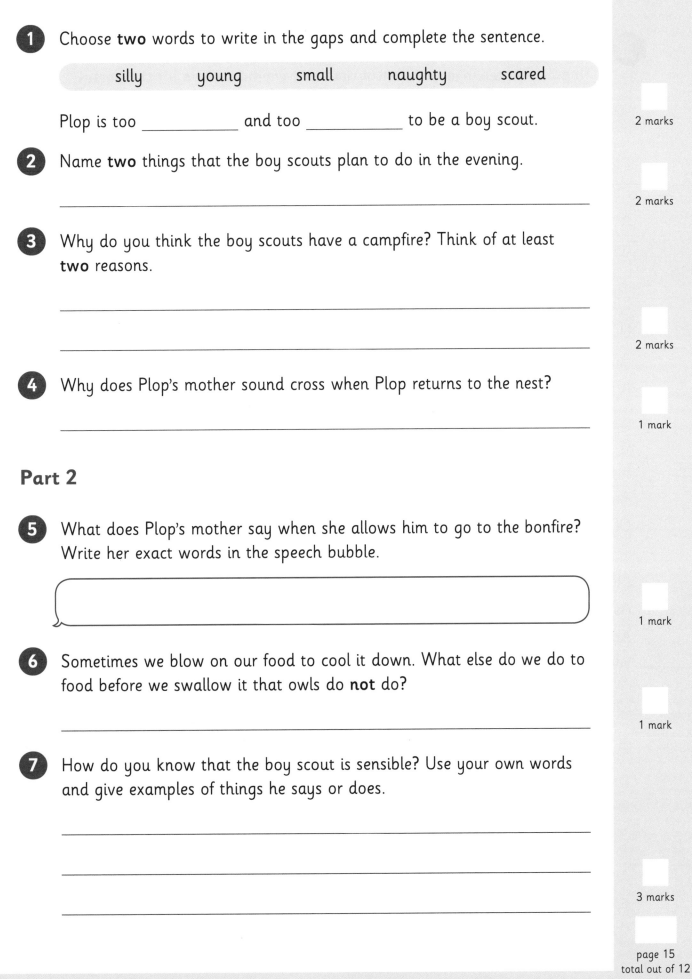

1 mark

6 Sometimes we blow on our food to cool it down. What else do we do to food before we swallow it that owls do **not** do?

_____

1 mark

7 How do you know that the boy scout is sensible? Use your own words and give examples of things he says or does.

_____

_____

_____

3 marks

page 15
total out of 12

I love my darling tractor

 Before farmers had tractors, they harnessed farm tools to horses for them to pull. Farmers needed a lot of time and energy to care for the horses, but a tractor is much easier to look after.

I love my darling tractor,
I love its merry din,
Its muscles made of iron and steel,
Its red and yellow skin.

I love to watch its wheels go round
However hard the day,
And from its bed inside the shed
It never thinks to stray.

It saves my arm, it saves my leg,
It saves my back from toil,
And it's merry as a **skink** when I give it a drink
Of water and diesel oil.

I love my darling tractor
As you can clearly see,
And so, the jolly farmer said,
Would you if you were me.

Charles Causley (1917–2003)

Glossary

skink a kind of lizard that is found in hot countries

Part 1

1 Who is talking about the 'darling tractor'?

_____

1 mark

2 a) Complete this phrase with the word that the poet uses for 'noise'.

'I love its merry _____ .'

1 mark

b) The poet puts this word with the word 'merry' to make the tractor sound (ring **one**):

tired and worn out   cheerful and strong   loud and dangerous.

1 mark

3 Which human body parts does the poet say the tractor has, to make it sound alive?

_____

2 marks

Part 2

4 Where is the tractor kept at night? _____

1 mark

5 The tractor 'never thinks to stray'. What does 'stray' mean? (ring **one**)

play the fool   wander off   break down

1 mark

6 When the owner puts oil and water in the tractor, he says he gives 'it a drink'. What does this tell us about his feelings for the tractor?

_____

_____

2 marks

7 📖 In the third verse, which word means 'work' or 'labour'?

_____

1 mark

page 17
total out of 10

17

Keeping warm in bed

 When you go to bed at night you expect to be snug, warm and cosy. Beds in the past were very different from those that we know today — some of them sound more comfortable than others.

Asleep with the sheep

In the past, people who lived in cold countries shared their houses with their farm animals. In wintertime, the animals were brought inside.

Some families slept on a platform above the animals. It was smelly up there, but it was warm.

My bed is a box!

About 300 years ago many people lived in draughty stone cottages. One way of keeping warm at night was to sleep in a box bed. These beds were built inside a big cupboard near the fire.

My bed is a tent!

Some rich and powerful people lived in palaces and slept in great big four-poster beds. Thick heavy curtains hung all around the bed to keep the draughts out. Beds like these were very expensive.

Warming the bed

What warms *your* bed on chilly nights? A snug electric blanket? A nice soft hot-water bottle? But what did people do before these things were invented?

Rich people sometimes made a servant get into their bed first to warm it up. A warming pan, with hot coals inside, could be used instead. A hot brick wrapped in a cloth was another way to warm the bed.

Hot-water bottles made of pottery were useful for warming the sheets. But they often leaked. Curved hot-water bottles were called 'belly warmers'.

From *Snug as a Bug*
Mal Peet and Elspeth Graham

Part 1

1 a) Why do you think people brought their farm animals inside the house in winter?

_____

1 mark

b) Why would it have been smelly, sleeping above the animals?

_____

1 mark

2 What was a box bed? **In your own words**, explain **when** and **why** people used them.

_____

_____

_____

3 marks

Part 2

3 a) Look at the picture. What sort of bed is this?

_____

1 mark

b) Why would only rich people have a bed like this?

_____

1 mark

4 Would you prefer to heat your bed with a modern hot-water bottle or a hot brick? Explain why.

_____

_____

3 marks

5 Describe **one** other old-fashioned way of heating a bed. Describe **one** problem with heating the bed this way.

_____

_____

2 marks

page 19
total out of 12

An adventure for Brave Mouse

 This story comes from a book called *Brave Mouse*, written by Jeremy Strong. As Brave Mouse sets out on a big adventure, this episode is partly about saying goodbye.

One morning Brave Mouse was walking by the water when he made a wonderful discovery. A beautiful sailing boat had been washed up on the shore.

It was red with white sails, like seagull wings. Beside the mast was a little wheel. Brave Mouse gazed at the boat and his heart did a little dance.

Carefully, he folded the sails and moved the boat to a safe place. Then he went home and called for his wife and son.

"I have great news," said Brave Mouse. "I am going to sail round the world."

Mrs Mouse burst into tears and wrung her tail. Tiny Mouse jumped up and down. He wanted to go with his father.

Brave Mouse shook his head.

"You are too young to come with me this time," he said. "I am going to sail round the world single-pawed."

Brave Mouse worked hard to get the little boat ready for the long ocean voyage. He put in a hard-boiled egg, some cheesy biscuits and a photograph of his wife and child.

That same evening, as the sun began to set, Brave Mouse set off. The warm wind pushed out the sails and he pointed the boat out to sea.

Mrs Mouse and Tiny Mouse stood on the shore. They waved their hankies until they could no longer see the little red boat in the fading light. The great adventure had begun.

From *Brave Mouse*
Jeremy Strong

Part 1

1 Which members of Brave Mouse's family are mentioned in the text?

_____

2 What parts of the boat help it to move with wind power?

_____

3 Brave Mouse's heart 'did a little dance' because he (ring **one**):

    wanted to sing   felt sick   had an exciting thought   panicked.

4 Mrs Mouse is upset. How do you know this from the story?

_____

_____

5 Why do you think Mrs Mouse is upset?

_____

Part 2

6 How do you know that Brave Mouse is planning to sail all by himself?
Give **one** reason.

_____

7 What did Brave Mouse take with him on his voyage? (ring **two**)

    phone   clothing   food   camera   photograph   compass

8 What sort of story do you think this text is from? (ring **two**)

    science fiction   historical   fantasy   biography   adventure

The four friends

This poem is written by the author who wrote stories and poems about Winnie the Pooh. The animals in this poem are very different from each other but, as the title says, they are friends all the same.

Ernest was an elephant, a great big fellow,
 Leonard was a lion with a six-foot tail,
George was a goat, and his beard was yellow,
    And James was a very small snail.

Leonard had a stall, and a great big strong one,
 Ernest had a **manger**, and its walls were thick,
George found a pen, but I think it was the wrong one,
    And James sat down on a brick.

Ernest started trumpeting, and cracked his manger,
 Leonard started roaring, and shivered his stall,
James gave the huffle of a snail in danger
    And nobody heard him at all.

Ernest started trumpeting and raised such a **rumpus**,
 Leonard started roaring and trying to kick,
James went on a journey with the goat's new compass
    And he reached the end of his brick.

Ernest was an elephant and very well-intentioned,
 Leonard was a lion with a brave new tail,
George was a goat, as I think I have mentioned,
    But James was only a snail.

A. A. Milne (1882–1956)

Glossary

manger an animal's feeding container
rumpus a noisy disturbance

Schofield & Sims **First Comprehension** Book 1

Part 1

1 Who is the largest character in the poem and what animal is he?

_____

2 marks

2 What is the name of the snail?

_____

1 mark

3 Fill in the gaps in the sentence below:

The _____ roars and the elephant _____ .

2 marks

4 Why do you think nobody hears James's 'huffle'?

_____

1 mark

Part 2

5 What did George lend to James to help him on his journey?

_____

1 mark

6 Read these statements. Each is either 'true' or 'false'. Put a tick in the correct box.

Tick one box only for each statement	True	False
a) George has a red beard.		
b) The lion is trying to kick.		
c) The elephant is painting his manger.		
d) Ernest means well.		
e) A 'rumpus' is a noisy disturbance.		

5 marks

What makes me move?

Your body is made up of lots of different parts, such as organs, muscles and nerves. Each part has a special job to do. This text explains how bones and muscles work together to enable us to move.

Bones

If you feel your head, your chest or your hands, you can feel hard parts under your skin. These are your bones. Your skeleton is made up of 206 bones.

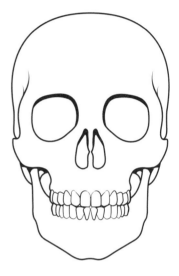

Without a skeleton you would be floppy and unable to move. Your skeleton supports and protects your body – your skull protects your brain, and your ribs protect your heart and lungs.

When you were born, your bones were very small. As you got older, the bones in your skeleton got bigger. Your bones will continue to grow until you are about 18 years old.

If you eat plenty of fresh fruit, green vegetables and cheese, you will help to keep your bones healthy.

Muscles

Your bones are very important, but they could not move without muscles. You have over 600 muscles in your body. You use them every time you move, whether you are kicking a ball, smiling or blinking.

Muscles are stretchy, like elastic. They bend and stretch when you use them. If you bend and straighten your arm, you can feel the muscle at the top of your arm bend and stretch. This muscle is called the biceps. You can also feel the muscles in your face. Put your hands on your face and smile. Now frown. Can you feel the muscles move?

You cannot control all your muscles like this. On a cold day, you don't try to shiver by moving your muscles – they move **automatically**. Other muscles move food through your body when you eat. Your heart is also a muscle. It keeps moving all day and all night to pump blood through your body.

> **Glossary**
> automatically naturally, without active effort

Part 1

1 Add the missing words.

My skeleton is a collection of _____ all joined together.

My body would be floppy if I did not have a _____ .

I could not move a bone in my body if I did not have _____ .

2 Which part of your body does your skull protect?

_____

1 mark

3 Colour in the one food below that is good for your bones.

Explain why you chose that one.

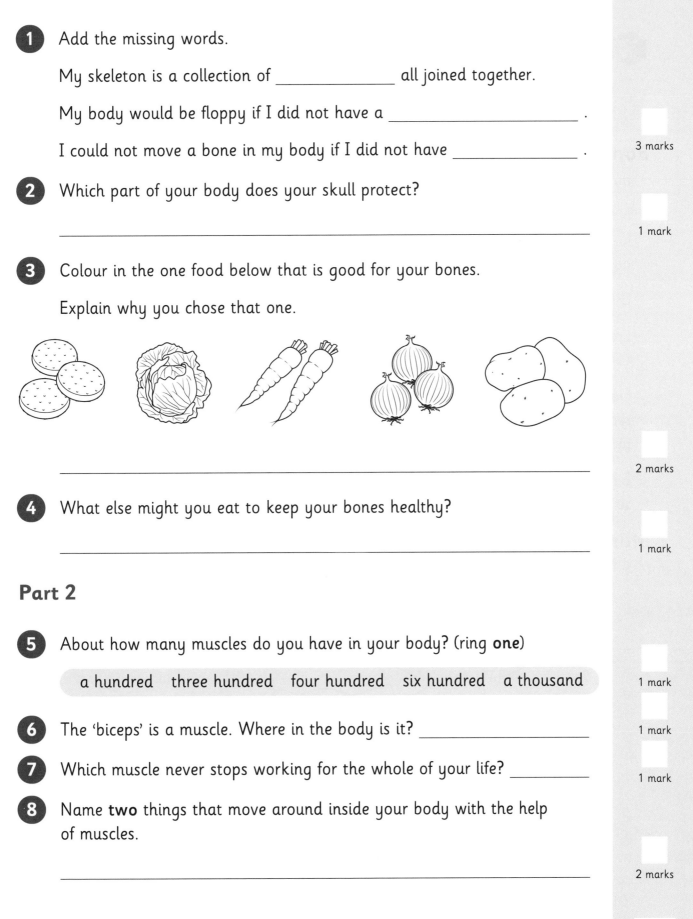

_____

2 marks

4 What else might you eat to keep your bones healthy?

_____

1 mark

Part 2

5 About how many muscles do you have in your body? (ring **one**)

a hundred   three hundred   four hundred   six hundred   a thousand

1 mark

6 The 'biceps' is a muscle. Where in the body is it? _____

1 mark

7 Which muscle never stops working for the whole of your life? _____

1 mark

8 Name **two** things that move around inside your body with the help of muscles.

_____

2 marks

page 25
total out of 12

A very small beetle

A very small beetle with a very big name has spent the night in a strange object that he found under a hedge – an old boot. The beetle's name is Omnibombulator (*Om-nee-bom-byoo-lay-ter*).

A whiskery tramp had been trudging along the lane, after a night spent under a haystack, when he spied the old boot.

Now if there's one thing a tramp needs, it's a good pair of boots, and this tramp had a big hole in his left boot. The right boot was OK but the left one let in water all the time. And this old boot, the tramp saw with pleasure, was a left one.

But would it fit? He sat down on the grass verge to try it on.

Omnibombulator was shaken violently out of a deep sleep as the tramp picked up the old boot and shoved his foot into it.

Hastily Omnibombulator retreated before the huge advancing toes until he reached the inside of the toecap and could go no further. Desperately he pressed himself against its leather wall.

Because the boot was a fraction too big for the tramp's foot, and because he was so very small, Omnibombulator survived.

He was in total darkness, jammed against a very dirty big toe that stuck through a hole in the tramp's sock, and the smell was simply awful.

From *Omnibombulator*
Dick King-Smith (1922–2011)

Part 1

1 Where had the tramp slept the night before he found the boot?

_____

2 Which part of the tramp's body might be 'whiskery' and why?

_____

_____

3 a) Why does the tramp need a new boot?

_____

b) Do you think the tramp would walk through puddles or go round them? Explain your answer.

_____

_____

4 What is the old boot made of? _____

Part 2

5 How well does the boot fit the tramp's foot? (ring **one**)

a little too small   a perfect fit   a little too large

6 Which word tells us that Omnibombulator lived through this adventure?

He _____ .

7 The tramp had been 'trudging' along the lane. Why is 'trudging' a better word than 'walking'?

_____

8 How do you think Omnibombulator feels after the tramp puts the boot on? Explain your answer.

_____

_____

Birdsong lullaby

 There are some sounds you can only hear when everything is quiet and no-one is talking. This poem describes sounds and feelings at a sleepy time of day.

As evening comes and blue light tints the sky

sleepily I listen for the birdsong lullaby.

Waiting by my window I feel the cool twilight,

hear the fidgeting of insects

who love to dance at night.

Then begins the singing, especially for me.

One bird's little solo becomes a choir tree.

'Chirr-up!', 'Chirr-up!', 'Cheer up!',

they seem to say.

Put drowsy head on pillow

while we sing the day away.

Pauline Stewart

Part 1

1 What time of day is it in the poem? _____   1 mark

2 A lullaby helps the listener to (ring **one**):

learn the words   hear music   go to sleep   sing like a bird.   1 mark

3 Which word shows that the insects are constantly moving as they 'dance'?

_____   1 mark

4 Write out the line in the poem that tells you that one bird starts singing, and then the other birds join in.

_____

_____   1 mark

Part 2

5 Which words describe the atmosphere of this poem? (ring **two**)

sleepy   sad   calm   lonely   angry   2 marks

6 📖 The word 'twilight' means (ring **one**):

summer   dawn   dusk   breeze   moonlight.   1 mark

7 Which **two** real words does the bird's 'Chirr-up' sound like?

_____   2 marks

8 Which word in the poem means the same as 'sleepy'?

_____   1 mark

Beyond the castle walls

Travel back in time around 800 years to look at a typical English castle. There are still castles like the one described in this text all over the country, and many of them welcome visitors.

It is almost impossible for an enemy to get into the castle. Behind the wall at the back is a steep cliff. Round the front and the sides are a deep ditch and two rows of heavily defended walls. What you find beyond the gates is almost a little town. The castle has its own carpenters and its own thatchers and masons to keep the thatched roofs and stone walls repaired. It has shoemakers and blacksmiths, tailors and armourers. There are stables, water, food supplies — even a fishpond. If you were besieged, you might live here quite comfortably for weeks.

Sentries patrolling the walkway behind the battlements can see for miles. But the wind can be bitterly cold, so there are sentry-boxes to shelter them, and sometimes ovens to keep their food warm.

The keep is the strongest part of the castle. Its walls are three metres thick and it has no doors or windows near the ground. An attacker climbing the stair would have his sword arm against the wall. It would be hard for him to defend himself.

From *Knights and Castles*
Toni Goffe

A foot soldier tries to attack the castle

Schofield & Sims **First Comprehension** Book 1

Part 1

1 📖 If a castle is surrounded by attackers trying to capture it, it is (ring **one**):

> impossible   repaired   besieged   patrolled.

2 Which of these people looks after the thatched roof? (ring **one**)

> mason   thatcher   carpenter   blacksmith

3 Name **two** other workers whom you might find inside a castle.

_____

4 Which part of the castle has walls that are three metres thick?

_____

5 Explain why people living within the castle wall would feel as if they were living in a small town.

_____

_____

Part 2

6 a) Even if no-one attacks the castle, it could be uncomfortable on sentry-duty. Explain why.

_____

b) How are sentries made more comfortable?

_____

7 a) What does 'sword arm' mean?

_____

b) Most people's sword arm was their right arm. Draw a sword in the attacker's left hand on page 30. How does it help him to be left-handed?

_____

Stop thief!

➡️ Barney has made friends with Stig, who lives in an old chalk pit. He seems to be a caveman, who can't speak or understand English. When Barney finds a thief in his granny's house, he rushes off to ask Stig for help.

Barney could see no signs of anyone coming after him, so he got up and plunged through the **copse**. Look out, bluebells and primroses! he thought, I'm in a hurry!

By the time he had got round the **down** into the pit, and along the bottom to Stig's cave, he was quite out of breath.

Stig was there all right. There was a strong smell coming from something gluey he was melting on the fire. He was sticking arrow-heads on to their shafts and binding them with catgut which he was taking from a broken old tennis racket. He looked all ready for the spring hunting season.

"Stig!" puffed Barney. "Thank goodness you're here! You've got to help! A man's got into Granny's house and I'm sure he's a thief and he'll take all the silver and jewels and even my money box if he finds it and it's got **three and threepence** in it. What are we going to do, Stig?"

Stig just grinned in a friendly way and Barney began to feel hopeless. It was just like when he was trying to explain about Stig to the grown-ups – they just smiled and said "Really?" And of course Stig didn't speak English. He didn't talk at all much. But he must make him understand.

"Enemy!" said Barney fiercely, pointing towards the top of the cliff. "Bad men!" he said, screwing up his face to look wicked. "Fight 'em, Stig, shoot 'em, see 'em off Stig," he urged, making bow-and-arrow movements and spear movements with his arms.

Stig seemed to get the idea.

From *Stig of the Dump*
Clive King

Glossary

copse a small wood; a group of trees
down a hill without trees, often grassy chalkland
three and threepence three shillings and three pence, in old British coins (16¼p)

Part 1

1 Why does Barney warn the flowers to 'look out' as he runs?

_____

1 mark

2 'Stig was there all right' suggests that (ring **one**):

Stig is feeling well   Barney expects Stig to be there, and he is

Stig is right-handed.

1 mark

3 Before Stig ties the arrow-heads to the shafts, what does he do to fix them in place?

_____

1 mark

4 Which word tells us that Barney is out of breath when he speaks to Stig?

_____

1 mark

Part 2

5 Why does Stig 'just grin' when Barney tells him about the thief?

_____

1 mark

6 Do you think Barney's family believe he has a friend who is a caveman? Explain your answer.

_____

_____

2 marks

7 How does Barney make Stig understand:

a) **where** the problem is? _____

b) **what** the problem is? _____

c) **how** he thinks Stig could help? _____

_____

3 marks

page 33
total out of 10

The months

Christina Rossetti, who wrote this poem, lived during the reign of Queen Victoria. Born in London, the poet was familiar with the British climate. Here she describes each month of the year.

January cold desolate;

February all dripping wet;

March wind ranges;

April changes;

Birds sing in tune

To flowers of May,

And sunny June

Brings longest day;

In scorched July

The storm-clouds fly

Lightning torn;

August bears corn,

September fruit;

In rough October

Earth must disrobe her;

Stars fall and shoot

In keen November;

And night is long

And cold is strong

In bleak December.

Christina Rossetti (1830—1894)

Schofield & Sims **First Comprehension** Book 1

Part 1

1 Which month does the poet think is windy? _____

2 a) In which month must 'Earth … disrobe her' (undress herself)?

_____

b) How does the Earth 'disrobe'? (ring **two**)

> flowers die   snow falls   trees lose their leaves
> rain makes the ground muddy

3 What does the poet say the birds are singing to? Colour it in below.

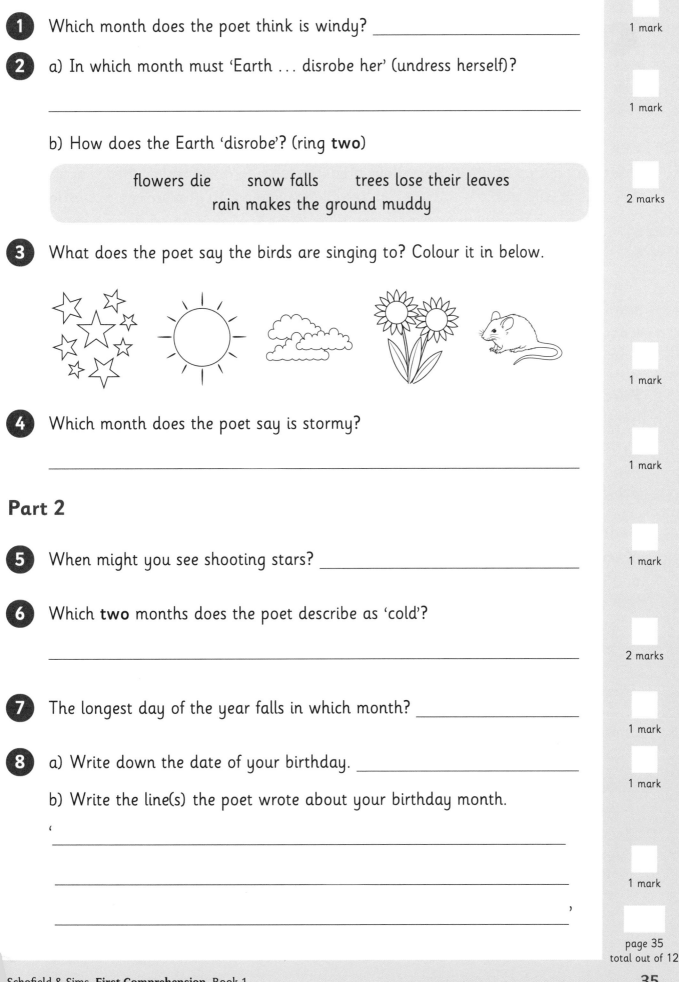

4 Which month does the poet say is stormy?

_____

Part 2

5 When might you see shooting stars? _____

6 Which **two** months does the poet describe as 'cold'?

_____

7 The longest day of the year falls in which month? _____

8 a) Write down the date of your birthday. _____

b) Write the line(s) the poet wrote about your birthday month.

'

_____

_____

_____ '

Jeremy Strong's world

 Jeremy Strong has written lots of story books for children. There is a text from one of his stories, *Brave Mouse*, on page 20 of this book. In **First Comprehension Book 2**, the text 'Bird meets chimpanzee' (on page 20) comes from his comical children's novel, *The Beak Speaks*.

Routine I get up at about 8am, have breakfast and go down to my shed – or, as my wife calls it, the studio – to write. I'm terrible for finding **displacement activities**. I'll do washing up or ironing or almost anything. But once I'm writing I don't want to be interrupted.

Teachers I had a very **influential** primary school teacher. She encouraged us to write stories and I began to think this is what I want to do when I grow up. Without her I wouldn't have got into writing at all – she said nice things about my stories and I wanted her to say more nice things.

Poetry When I was about 12 I was very bored one summer and found a poetry book that belonged to my older brother. I was thumbing through and came across *Further* **Reflections** *on Parsley* by Ogden Nash. It goes, 'Parsley / is gharsley'. It blew my mind. I thought, 'I didn't know you could do that with words and spelling' and **promptly** started looking for more poems.

Bedtime scribbles I always have notebooks by the bed. Occasionally a whole chunk of text will appear in my head at 2am – I'll have a conversation between characters and I have to get it down immediately. So sometimes that means getting a book out and writing for an hour or two. It's useful, but annoying.

Jeremy Strong
From *The Telegraph*, 31 May 2013

Glossary

displacement activity anything that a person does to avoid or delay doing something more important
influential having an important, powerful effect or impact
promptly without delay
reflections thoughts
routine regular repeated pattern and sequence of behaviour or actions

Part 1

1 Jeremy Strong is (ring **one**):

> an artist   an author   an illustrator   a singer.

1 mark

2 Colour the clock that shows when Jeremy gets up in the morning.

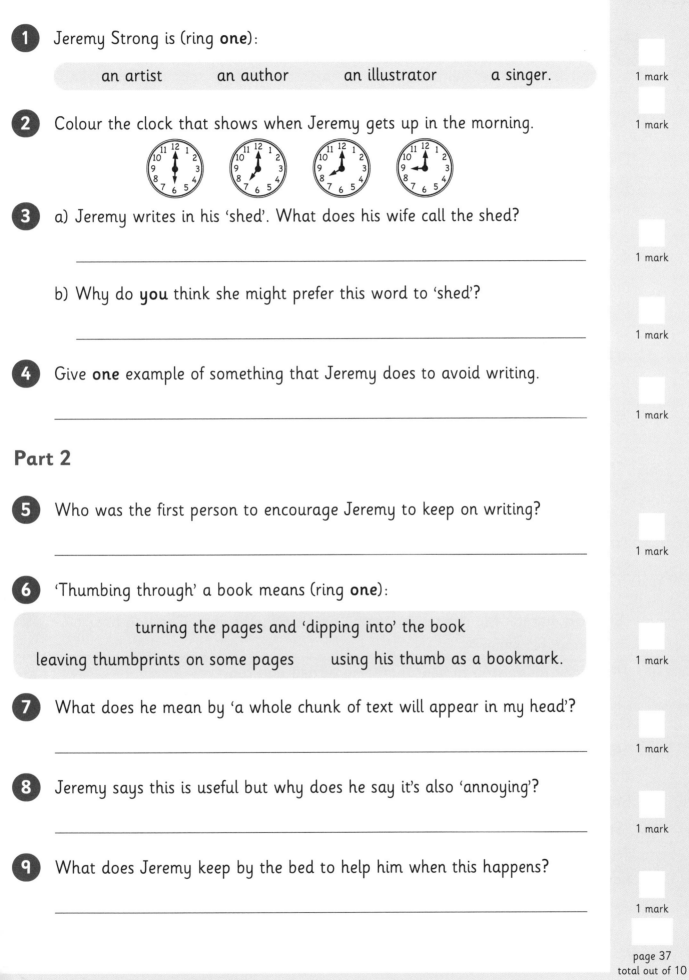

1 mark

3 a) Jeremy writes in his 'shed'. What does his wife call the shed?

_____

1 mark

b) Why do **you** think she might prefer this word to 'shed'?

_____

1 mark

4 Give **one** example of something that Jeremy does to avoid writing.

_____

1 mark

Part 2

5 Who was the first person to encourage Jeremy to keep on writing?

_____

1 mark

6 'Thumbing through' a book means (ring **one**):

> turning the pages and 'dipping into' the book
>
> leaving thumbprints on some pages   using his thumb as a bookmark.

1 mark

7 What does he mean by 'a whole chunk of text will appear in my head'?

_____

1 mark

8 Jeremy says this is useful but why does he say it's also 'annoying'?

_____

1 mark

9 What does Jeremy keep by the bed to help him when this happens?

_____

1 mark

page 37
total out of 10

Clever Gretel

This is a retelling of a fairy tale written by the Grimm Brothers. You may have read other famous stories by these storytellers, such as 'Cinderella', 'Little Red Riding Hood' and 'Sleeping Beauty'.

Once upon a time there was a cook called Gretel. She always helped herself to the best, and served her absent-minded master whatever was left. One day he invited a gentleman to dinner and told her to cook two chickens.

Soon the roasted chickens smelt delicious, but the guest had not arrived. As her master walked down the road to look for him, Gretel basted the birds with butter. She looked through the window. There was no sign of her master and the guest, so her gaze returned longingly to the chickens.

"That wing looks burnt," she told herself. "I'd better eat that."

It was so tasty, she tried a second wing. Gretel ran to the window: still no sign of her master!

"Perhaps the visitor isn't coming," she said. "I might as well finish this chicken."

Before long Gretel had eaten *both* chickens. Then her master returned.

"Hurry, Gretel. My guest is coming."

"Yes, master. Dinner is ready."

She could hear him sharpening the carving knife. Before his guest had time to knock, Gretel opened the door. She put a finger to her lips.

"Shh! Go quickly. My master's planning to cut off your ears. Can you hear him sharpening his knife?"

The visitor didn't stop to hear more. He turned and ran.

Gretel rushed to her master.

"Alas!" she cried. "Your guest has stolen the roast chickens. He's running down the street with them."

Still holding the knife, Gretel's master rushed after him.

"Stop, stop! At least let me have *one* of them."

The guest thought he meant one *ear*. He didn't stop running till he was safely home with the door bolted.

Based on a story by the Grimm Brothers

Schofield & Sims **First Comprehension** Book 1

Part 1

1 The title describes Gretel as 'clever'. What word(s) would **you** use to describe her? Explain why.

_____

_____

2 Explain the meaning of 'absent-minded' **in your own words**, by completing this sentence.

An absent-minded person is someone who _____

_____.

3 The chicken wing looks burnt. Why does this seem like a good excuse for Gretel to eat it herself?

_____

4 The master calls his visitor his _____.

Part 2

5 Why is Gretel keen to reach the door before the visitor knocks?

_____

6 Why is Gretel's master sharpening his knife?

_____

7 If her master had answered the door, the story might have had a different ending. Explain what might have happened and why.

_____

_____

8 When the master cries, 'At least let me have _one_ of them', what is he talking about?

_____

Schofield&Sims

the long-established educational publisher specialising in maths, English and science

First Comprehension provides an early introduction to written comprehension, developing children's enthusiasm for reading and their ability to interpret texts. When working through the series, support from an adult will boost children's confidence and help them to understand and evaluate each text. The books are easy to mark and provide a permanent record of each child's work, helping you to monitor progress.

Designed to support the National Curriculum for Years 2 and 3, the content of this series has wide appeal and may also be used by older children.

The series provides:

- a **brief introduction**, enabling teachers, parents and adult helpers to use the books effectively

- passages from **classic and contemporary fiction** to broaden children's reading experience

- a wide selection of **poetry**, from William Wordsworth to Tony Mitton

- stimulating **non-fiction** extracts, with different subjects and structures

- a **range of question types**, including direct, inferential and evaluative questions.

First Comprehension Book 1 is aimed at children in Year 2 (ages 6–7) who are attempting written comprehension for the first time. Eighteen carefully selected texts reflect the range of genres recommended by the National Curriculum, and accompanying questions are presented in two parts, to suit the concentration level of most children in this age group. The first of two **First Comprehension** activity books, this book features work by writers such as Roald Dahl and A. A. Milne, as well as an excerpt from a children's dictionary and a number of accessible non-fiction texts.

The separate **Teacher's Guide** contains teaching notes, sample answers and further activities for each text, allowing you to use **First Comprehension** to its full potential.

The full range of books in the series is as follows.

First Comprehension Book 1   ISBN 978 07217 1220 8
First Comprehension Book 2   ISBN 978 07217 1221 5
First Comprehension Teacher's Guide   ISBN 978 07217 1222 2

Key Stage 2 Comprehension is available for older children.

ISBN 978-07217-1220-8

FSC® C023114
MIX
Paper from responsible sources

ISBN 978 07217 1220 8
Key Stages 1 & 2
Age range: 6–8 years
£3.95 (Retail price)

For further information and to place your order visit
www.schofieldandsims.co.uk or telephone 01484 607080